Latin leads

Many English words have prefixes that came fro
trans meant across, **sub** meant under and **ex** meant out of.

■ Match each ending on the aqueduct to the correct prefix.
Write the completed words in the correct arch.

clude	asperate	late	urb
stitute	port	lucent	hibit
marine	aggerate	parent	ordinate
mitter	conscious	cursion	

trans

- - - - - - - - -
- - - - - - - - -
- - - - - - - - -
- - - - - - - - -
- - - - - - - - -

sub

- - - - - - - - -
- - - - - - - - -
- - - - - - - - -
- - - - - - - - -
- - - - - - - - -

ex

- - - - - - - - -
- - - - - - - - -
- - - - - - - - -
- - - - - - - - -
- - - - - - - - -

■ Use look, say, cover, write, check to practise each word.

_____ _____ _____

_____ _____ _____

_____ _____ _____

_____ _____ _____

_____ _____ _____

Tick here when you have checked your work. ☐

Greek ghosts

These words have Greek prefixes which help you find their meanings.

■ Match the correct Greek prefix in the haunted tower to each ghost.

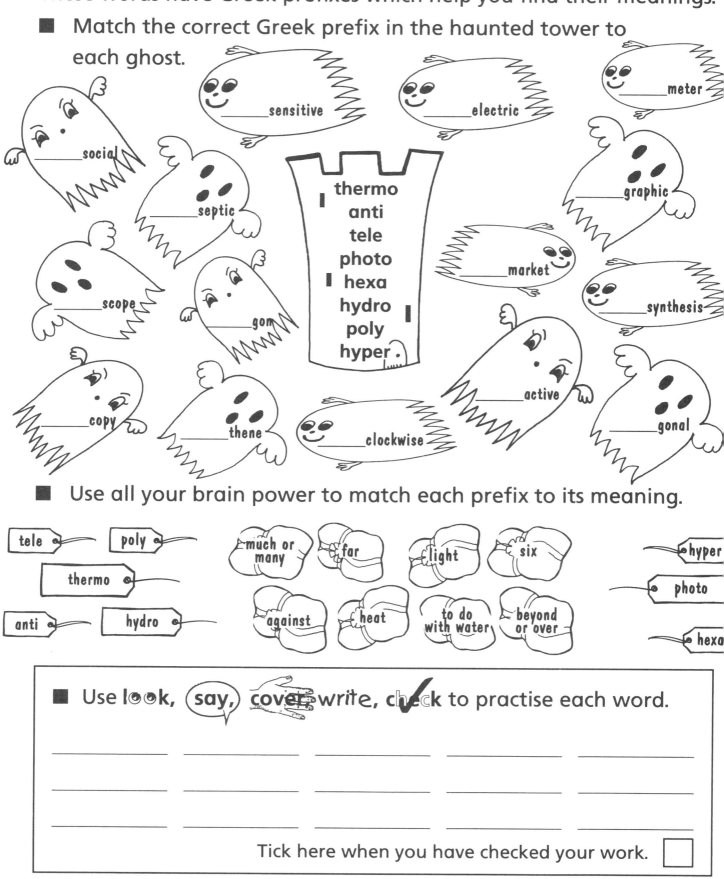

■ Use all your brain power to match each prefix to its meaning.

tele   poly   much or many   far   light   six   hyper

thermo   against   heat   to do with water   beyond or over   photo

anti   hydro   hexa

■ Use look, say, cover, write, check to practise each word.

_____ _____ _____ _____ _____

_____ _____ _____ _____ _____

_____ _____ _____ _____ _____

Tick here when you have checked your work. ☐

Exciting excerpts

■ The cameraman has cut out all the **exc** beginnings to these words. Edit the film to find the endings and write out the completed word.

| i t i n g e r p t u s e e e d e s s i v e e l l e n c e |

| i s e h a n g e h e q u e r e p t i o n a l l u s i o n |

| r u c i a t i n g o m m u n i c a t e l a i m u r s i o n |

exc _iting_   exc _hequer_

exc _____   exc _____

exc _____   exc _____

exc _____   exc _____

exc _____   exc _____

exc _____   exc _laim_

exc _____   exc _____

exc _____

■ Arrange these words in alphabetical order.

1 _____   9 _____
2 _____   10 _____
3 _____   11 _____
4 _____   12 _____
5 _____   13 _____
6 _____   14 _____
7 _____   15 _____
8 _____

■ Use look, (say,) cover, write, check to practise each word.

_____ _____ _____ _____

_____ _____ _____ _____

_____ _____ _____ _____

_____ _____ _____

Tick here when you have checked your work. ☐

Mysterious Morse!

words

The Morse code was invented to send messages over long distances. It is a system of dots and dashes.

a	•—	b	—•••	c	—•—•	d	—••	e	•	f	••—•	g	——•	h	••••	i	••
j	•———	k	—•—	l	•—••	m	——	n	—•	o	———	p	•——•	q	——•—	r	•—•
s	•••	t	—	u	••—	v	•••—	w	•——	x	—••—	y	—•——	z	——••

■ Decode these words.

•——•	•••	—•——	—•—•	••••	••	•—	—	•—•	••	•••	—

= _____

•——•	•••	—•——	—•—•	••••	———	•—••	———	——•	—•——

= _____

•——•	•••	•	••—	—••	———	—•	—•——	——

= _____

•——•	•••	———	•—•	••	•—	•••	••	•••

= _____

•——•	•••	—•——	—•—•	••••	———	—	••	—•—•

= _____

•——•	•••	—•——	—•—•	••••	••	—•—

= _____

•——•	•••	—•——	—•—•	••••	•

= _____

•——•	•••	•—	•—••	——

= _____

■ Use look, (say,) cover, write, check to practise each word.

_____   _____   _____   _____

_____   _____   _____   _____

Tick here when you have checked your work. ☐

Page 6

Accidents with acc

■ The computer has accidentally axed all the vowels from these **acc** words. Use the clues below the screen to repair each word.

1 *cc*mm*d*t**n
_ _ _ _ _ _ _ _ _ _ _
Help: living quarters or lodgings

2 *cc*l*r*t*
_ _ _ _ _ _ _ _ _
Help: to speed up

3 *cc*pt*bl*
_ _ _ _ _ _ _ _ _
Help: worth accepting

4 *cc*ss
_ _ _ _ _ _
Help: entry into

5 *cc*s*t**n
_ _ _ _ _ _ _ _ _
Help: a statement blaming someone

6 *cc*st*m*d
_ _ _ _ _ _ _ _ _ _
Help: used to it happening

7 *cc*m*l*t*
_ _ _ _ _ _ _ _ _ _
Help: to heap or pile up

8 *cc*nt
_ _ _ _ _ _
Help: way of speaking particular to an area

9 *cc*d*nt
_ _ _ _ _ _ _ _
Help: a mishap or mistake

10 *cc*pt*nc*
_ _ _ _ _ _ _ _ _ _
Help: agreeing to terms

11 *cc**nt
_ _ _ _ _ _ _
Help: money in a bank

12 *cc*mpl*shm*nt
_ _ _ _ _ _ _ _ _ _ _ _ _ _
Help: an achievement

13 *cc*s*
_ _ _ _ _ _
Help: to blame someone

14 *cc*nt**t*
_ _ _ _ _ _ _ _ _ _
Help: to emphasise

15 *cc*rd**n
_ _ _ _ _ _ _ _ _
Help: a portable, squeezable musical instrument

■ Use look, say, cover, write, check to practise each word.

_ _ _ _ _ _ _ _ _ _   _ _ _ _ _ _ _ _ _ _   _ _ _ _ _ _ _ _ _ _

_ _ _ _ _ _ _ _ _ _   _ _ _ _ _ _ _ _ _ _   _ _ _ _ _ _ _ _ _ _

_ _ _ _ _ _ _ _ _ _   _ _ _ _ _ _ _ _ _ _   _ _ _ _ _ _ _ _ _ _

_ _ _ _ _ _ _ _ _ _   _ _ _ _ _ _ _ _ _ _   _ _ _ _ _ _ _ _ _ _

_ _ _ _ _ _ _ _ _ _   _ _ _ _ _ _ _ _ _ _

Tick here when you have checked your work. ☐

Syllable search

■ Join each prefix on the boot to as many endings on the footprints as you can to build two-syllable words.
You should find **16** words in total.

Write the words here

Prefixes

con

in

re

de

Endings

fect

flict

serve

struct

form

tour

_____
_____
_____
_____
_____
_____
_____
_____
_____
_____
_____
_____
_____
_____
_____
_____

■ Use l**oo**k, (**say,**) cover, write, check to practise each word.

_____ _____ _____ _____
_____ _____ _____ _____
_____ _____ _____ _____
_____ _____ _____ _____

Tick here when you have checked your work. ☐

Tricky teasers

■ The words in this crossword can be tricky to spell.
Use the clues to complete the crossword.

ACROSS

3. a sense of right and wrong (10)
6. hurt someone's feelings (6)
7. feeling isolated (6)
8. to repay an equivalent amount (10)
9. something which makes no sense (8)
11. three minus two (3)
14. not cheap (9)
16. opposite of unfriendly (8)
17. considerate (10)
18. He was no _ _ _ _ _ to be found (5)

DOWN

1. opposite of floor (7)
2. absolutely huge (7)
3. substance in cola and coffee (8)
4. to make smaller and more dense (8)
5. funny (7)
10. zero (7)
12. too much (9)
13. very concentrated or emotional (7)
15. to gain money or goods when someone dies (7)

■ Use look, say, cover, write, check to practise each word.

_____ _____ _____ _____ _____

_____ _____ _____ _____ _____

_____ _____ _____ _____

Tick here when you have checked your work. ☐

Double trouble

■ Match each umbrella to a cloud to make a compound word.

Umbrellas: heart, earth, white, ware, walk, iron, over, steam, mantel, whip, way, heavy

Clouds: piece, felt, house, lay, monger, weight, boat, about, wash, lash, quake, sight

■ Use look, say, cover, write, check to practise all the words.

_____   _____
_____   _____
_____   _____
_____   _____
_____   _____
_____   _____

Tick here when you have checked your work. ☐

Chaotic chemistry

In all these words the letters **ch** make a **k** sound.

■ Fit this list of **ch** words into the grid.

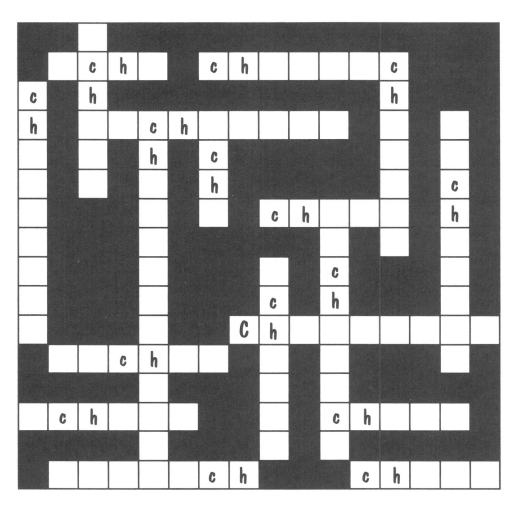

ache
anchor
architect
chaos
chaotic
character
chemist
choir
chord
Christmas
chrysanthemum
echo
orchestra
scheme
scholar
school
stomach
technical

■ Use look, (say,) cover, write, check to practise each word.

_____ _____ _____ _____ _____

_____ _____ _____ _____ _____

_____ _____ _____ _____ _____

_____ _____ Tick here when you have checked your work. ☐

Sound snap

■ Use each clue to write the word which sounds the same.
Try to write your own simple clue for the other card.

hear	_ _ _ _ (not there)
to	_ _ _ _ (a number)
bear	_ _ _ _ (naked)
none	_ _ _ _ (religious woman)
feet	_ _ _ _ (accompl-ishment)
our	_ _ _ _ (unit of time)
sweet	_ _ _ _ (sofa and chairs)
week	_ _ _ _ (not strong)
peace	_ _ _ _ (a bit of)
sore	_ _ _ _ (fly high)
grate	_ _ _ _ (very good)
heel	_ _ _ _ (make better)
sea	_ _ _ _ (sight)
practise	_ _ _ _ (the act of practising)

■ Use l👁👁k, (say,) cover, write, che✔k to practise each word pair.

_____ + _____   _____ + _____   _____ + _____

_____ + _____   _____ + _____   _____ + _____

_____ + _____   _____ + _____   _____ + _____

_____ + _____   _____ + _____   _____ + _____

_____ + _____   _____ + _____

Tick here when you have checked your work. ☐

Page 12

Problematic pasts

Some verbs change in unexpected ways to make the past tense.

■ The clues give the **present** tense. Fill in the past tense of each verb in the crossword. e.g.   <u>clue</u> **drive**   <u>answer</u> **drove**.

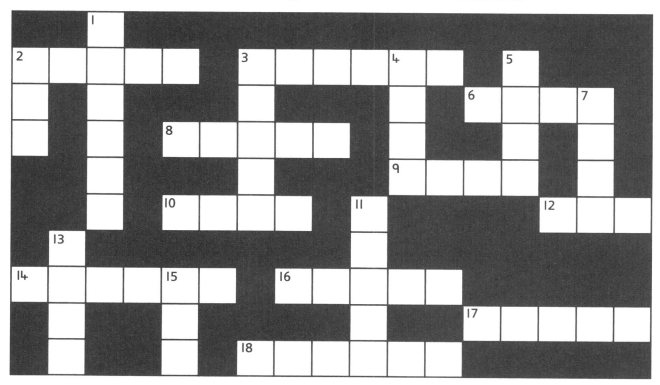

Clues Across

2. drive
3. seek
6. fly
8. shine
9. grow
10. draw
12. eat
14. catch
16. sting
17. throw
18. teach

Clues Down

1. buy
2. do
3. speak
4. hang
5. blow
7. go
11. fling
13. give
15. have

■ Use look, (say,) cover, write, check to practise each word.

_____   _____   _____   _____

_____   _____   _____   _____

_____   _____   _____   _____

_____   _____   _____   _____

_____   _____   _____   _____

Tick here when you have checked your work. ☐

Parcels of problems

■ These parcels contain anagrams of words many people make mistakes with. Use the letter boxes to help you to write each label.

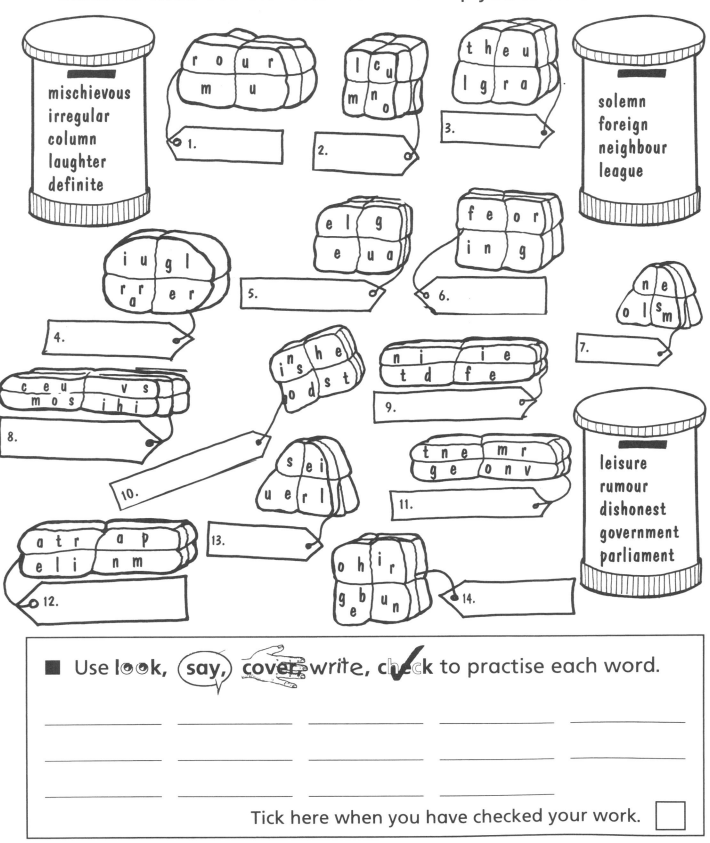

mischievous
irregular
column
laughter
definite

solemn
foreign
neighbour
league

leisure
rumour
dishonest
government
parliament

1.

2.

3.

4.

5.

6.

7.

8.

9.

10.

11.

12.

13.

14.

■ Use look, say, cover, write, check to practise each word.

_____   _____   _____   _____   _____

_____   _____   _____   _____   _____

_____   _____   _____   _____   _____

Tick here when you have checked your work. ☐

Double trouble 2

■ Match each toaster to a slice of bread to find twelve compound words.

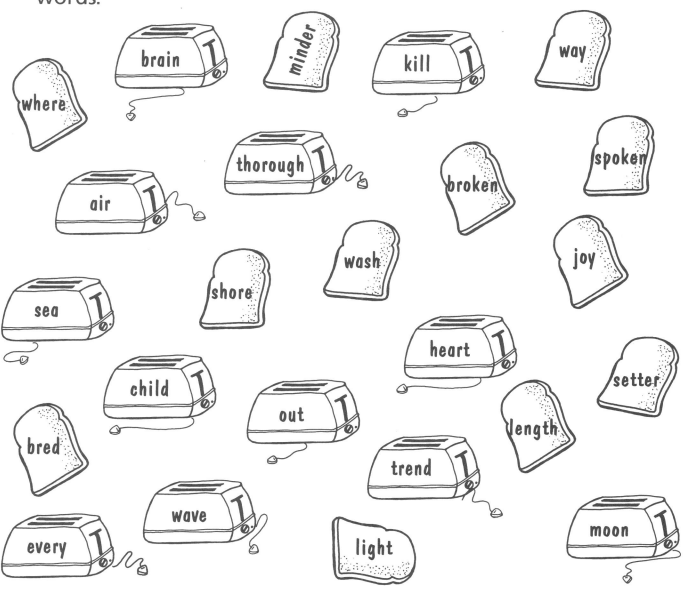

■ Use look, (say,) cover, write, check to practise each compound word.

_____ _____ _____

_____ _____ _____

_____ _____ _____

_____ _____ _____

Tick here when you have checked your work. ☐

Eccentric epidemic  **ic** words

■ Solve the clues to find the epidemic of **ic** words.

cyclic	academic	rheumatic	optimistic
systematic	electric	arthritic	problematic
arctic	pneumatic	scientific	hydraulic

at the north pole

a _ _ _ _ i c

alternative to gas for cooking

_ _ _ _ _ _ i c

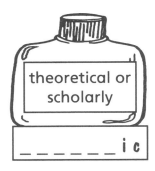
theoretical or scholarly

_ _ _ _ _ _ i c

relating to science

_ _ _ _ _ _ _ _ i c

happening in cycles

_ _ _ _ i c

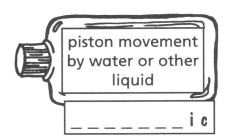
piston movement by water or other liquid

_ _ _ _ _ _ i c

movement caused by air in tubes

_ _ _ _ _ _ _ i c

affected by rheumatism

_ _ _ _ _ _ i c

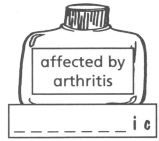
affected by arthritis

_ _ _ _ _ _ i c

filled with difficulties

_ _ _ _ _ _ _ _ i c

looking on the bright side

_ _ _ _ _ _ _ i c

methodical

_ _ _ _ _ _ _ _ i c

■ Use look, (say,) cover, write, check to practise each word.

_____ _____ _____ _____

_____ _____ _____ _____

_____ _____ _____ _____

Tick here when you have checked your work. ☐

New Spellaway 4

Key Stage 2

Answers

About New Spellaway

New Spellaway is a series of four books which progressively cover Key Stage 2 in Spelling. The puzzles are designed to provide short, fun, educational sessions and to complement the formal teaching of spelling. Positive adult support such as offering help, further explanation or providing a dictionary is invaluable to the student. The series also offers children the opportunity to consolidate each new pattern or concept through the multi-sensory look, say, cover, write, check approach. Children can be further encouraged to keep their own alphabetical list of words they have learned for their future reference.

You may wish to separate this answer section from the questions. Carefully pull out the middle 8 pages, then push the wire stitching back into place.

Latin leads

Page 3

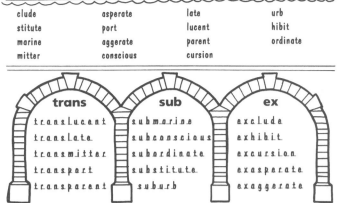

clude   asperate   late   urb
stitute port   lucent   hibit
marine aggerate   parent   ordinate
mitter conscious cursion

trans	sub	ex
translucent	submarine	exclude
translate	subconscious	exhibit
transmitter	subordinate	excursion
transport	substitute	exasperate
transparent	suburb	exaggerate

Greek ghosts

Page 4

photo sensitive
hydro electric
thermo meter
anti social
photo graphic
anti septic
tele scope
hexa gon
hyper market
photo synthesis
photo copy
poly thene
anti clockwise
hyper active
hexa gonal

thermo
anti
tele
photo
hexa
hydro
poly
hyper

tele — far
poly — much or many
thermo — heat
anti — against
hydro — to do with water
light — photo
six — hexa
beyond or over — hyper

Exciting excerpts

Page 5

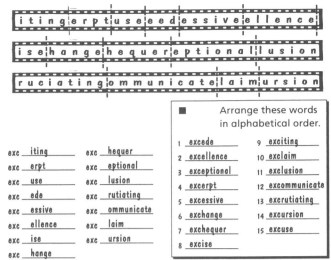

itingerptuseeedessiveellence

isehangehequereptionallusion

ruciatingommunicatelaimursion

Arrange these words in alphabetical order.

exc **iting**   exc **hequer**
exc **erpt**   exc **eptional**
exc **use**   exc **lusion**
exc **ede**   exc **rutiating**
exc **essive**   exc **ommunicate**
exc **ellence**   exc **laim**
exc **ise**   exc **ursion**
exc **hange**

1 excede
2 excellence
3 exceptional
4 excerpt
5 excessive
6 exchange
7 exchequer
8 excise
9 exciting
10 exclaim
11 exclusion
12 excommunicate
13 excrutiating
14 excursion
15 excuse

Mysterious Morse!

Page 6

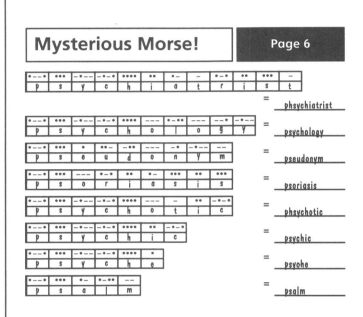

p s y c h i a t r i s t
= phsychiatrist

p s y c h o l o g y
= psychology

p s e u d o n y m
= pseudonym

p s o r i a s i s
= psoriasis

p s y c h o t i c
= phsychotic

p s y c h i c
= psychic

p s y c h e
= psyche

p s a l m
= psalm

Accidents with acc

Page 7

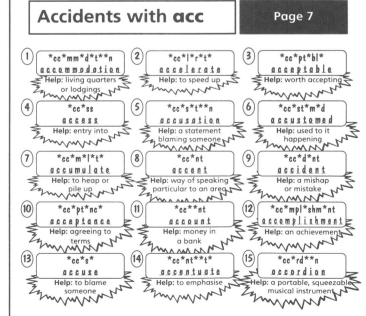

1) *cc*mm*d*t**n
accommodation
Help: living quarters or lodgings

2) *cc*l*r*t*
accelerate
Help: to speed up

3) *cc*pt*bl*
acceptable
Help: worth accepting

4) *cc*ss
access
Help: entry into

5) *cc*s*t**n
accusation
Help: a statement blaming someone

6) *cc*st*m*d
accustomed
Help: used to it happening

7) *cc*m*l*t*
accumulate
Help: to heap or pile up

8) *cc*nt
accent
Help: way of speaking particular to an area

9) *cc*d*nt
accident
Help: a mishap or mistake

10) *cc*pt*nc*
acceptance
Help: agreeing to terms

11) *cc**nt
account
Help: money in a bank

12) *cc*mpl*shm*nt
accomplishment
Help: an achievement

13) *cc*s*
accuse
Help: to blame someone

14) *cc*nt**t*
accentuate
Help: to emphasise

15) *cc*rd**n
accordion
Help: a portable, squeezable musical instrument

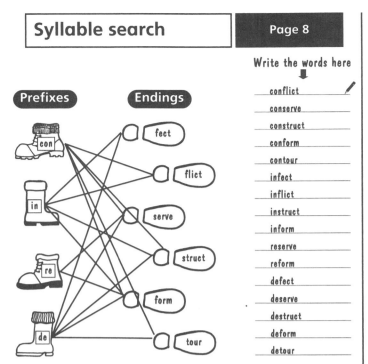

Prefixes | **Endings**

con, in, re, de

fect, flict, serve, struct, form, tour

Write the words here

- conflict
- conserve
- construct
- conform
- contour
- infect
- inflict
- instruct
- inform
- reserve
- reform
- defect
- deserve
- destruct
- deform
- detour

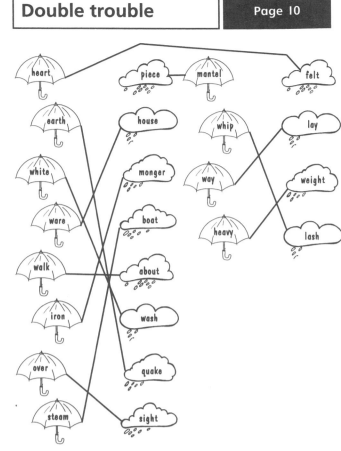

heart, piece, mantel, felt, earth, house, whip, lay, white, monger, way, weight, ware, boat, heavy, lash, walk, about, iron, wash, over, quake, steam, sight

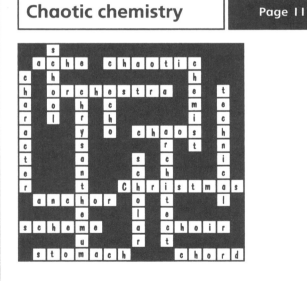

Answer page 3

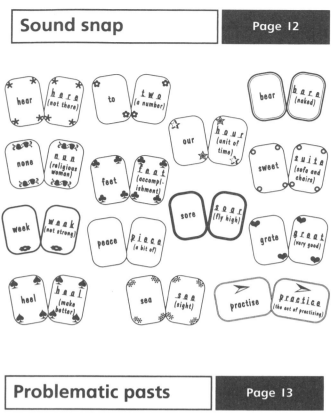

- hear / **here** (not there)
- to / **two** (a number)
- bear / **bare** (naked)
- none / **nun** (religious woman)
- our / **hour** (unit of time)
- sweet / **suite** (sofa and chairs)
- feet / **feat** (accomplishment)
- sore / **soar** (fly high)
- grate / **great** (very good)
- week / **weak** (not strong)
- peace / **piece** (a bit of)
- heel / **heal** (make better)
- sea / **see** (sight)
- practise / **practice** (the act of practising)

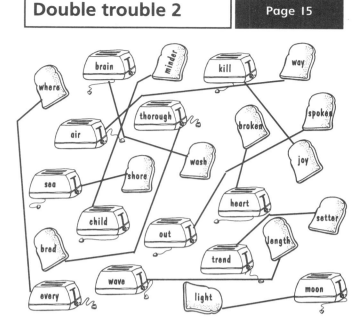

where, brain, minder, kill, way, air, thorough, broken, spoke, wash, joy, sea, shore, heart, setter, child, out, length, bred, trend, wave, every, light, moon

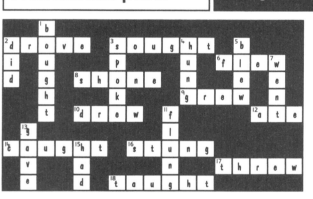

Crossword answers:
- 1. b (bought) / dug
- 2. drove
- 3. sought
- 4. t
- 5. b
- 6. flew
- 7. w
- 8. shone
- 9. grew
- 10. drew
- 11. f
- 12. ate
- 13. g
- 14. caught
- 15. h
- 16. stung
- 17. threw
- 18. taught

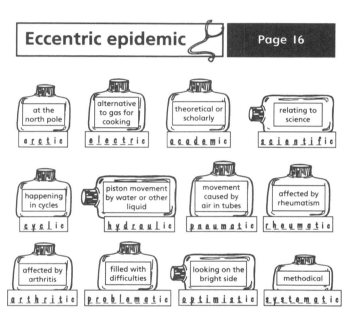

- at the north pole — **arctic**
- alternative to gas for cooking — **electric**
- theoretical or scholarly — **academic**
- relating to science — **scientific**
- happening in cycles — **cyclic**
- piston movement by water or other liquid — **hydraulic**
- movement caused by air in tubes — **pneumatic**
- affected by rheumatism — **rheumatic**
- affected by arthritis — **arthritic**
- filled with difficulties — **problematic**
- looking on the bright side — **optimistic**
- methodical — **systematic**

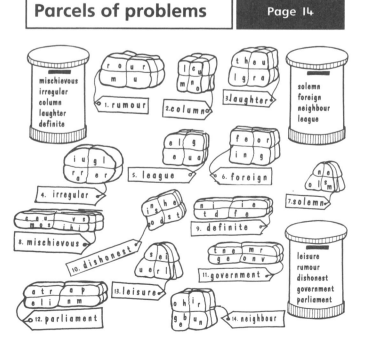

mischievous, irregular, column, laughter, definite

solemn, foreign, neighbour, league

leisure, rumour, dishonest, government, parliament

- 1. rumour
- 2. column
- 3. laughter
- 4. irregular
- 5. league
- 6. foreign
- 7. solemn
- 8. mischievous
- 9. definite
- 10. dishonest
- 11. government
- 12. parliament
- 13. leisure
- 14. neighbour

Influence of **ence**

1. Choosing one over another				p	r	e	f	e	r	e	n	c	e
2. A meeting for discussion					c	o	n	f	e	r	e	n	c	e
3. Distance round the outside of a circle	c	i	r	c	u	m	f	e	r	e	n	c	e
4. Dissimilarity					d	i	f	f	e	r	e	n	c	e
5. Formally begin						c	o	m	m	e	n	c	e
6. Done at your _____, or a W.C.			c	o	n	v	e	n	i	e	n	c	e
7. Requires a full stop at the end					s	e	n	t	e	n	c	e
8. Type of book for information				r	e	f	e	r	e	n	c	e
9. Moral sense or scruples			c	o	n	s	c	i	e	n	c	e
10. Extreme physical force					v	i	o	l	e	n	c	e
11. Treat yourself				i	n	d	u	l	g	e	n	c	e
12. State of not relying on others		i	n	d	e	p	e	n	d	e	n	c	e
13. Cheek!				i	m	p	u	d	e	n	c	e
14. Inability to wait			i	m	p	a	t	i	e	n	c	e
15. Harmlessness, freedom from guilt				i	n	n	o	c	e	n	c	e

Elementary discovery — Page 19

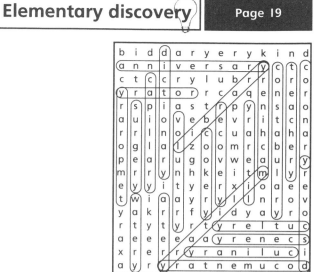

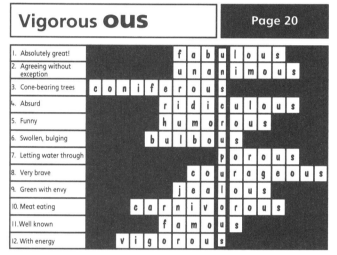

The **ance** alliance — Page 18

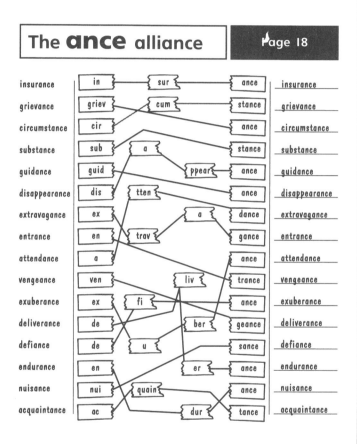

insurance → in · sur · ance → insurance
grievance → griev · cum · stance → grievance
circumstance → cir · ance → circumstance
substance → sub · a · stance → substance
guidance → guid · ppear · ance → guidance
disappearance → dis · tten · ance → disappearance
extravagance → ex · a · dance → extravagance
entrance → en · trav · gance → entrance
attendance → a · ance → attendance
vengeance → ven · liv · trance → vengeance
exuberance → ex · fi · ance → exuberance
deliverance → de · ber · geance → deliverance
defiance → de · u · sance → defiance
endurance → en · er · ance → endurance
nuisance → nui · quain · ance → nuisance
acquaintance → ac · dur · tance → acquaintance

Vigorous **ous** — Page 20

1. Absolutely great!						f	a	b	u	l	o	u	s
2. Agreeing without exception							u	n	a	n	i	m	o	u	s
3. Cone-bearing trees	c	o	n	i	f	e	r	o	u	s
4. Absurd						r	i	d	i	c	u	l	o	u	s
5. Funny						h	u	m	o	r	o	u	s
6. Swollen, bulging			b	u	l	b	o	u	s
7. Letting water through								p	o	r	o	u	s
8. Very brave					c	o	u	r	a	g	e	o	u	s
9. Green with envy				j	e	a	l	o	u	s
10. Meat eating		c	a	r	n	i	v	o	r	o	u	s
11. Well known						f	a	m	o	u	s
12. With energy			v	i	g	o	r	o	u	s

■ Look in a dictionary to find the meaning of **unscrupulous**.

withour regard to rules or to the needs of others

Puzzling plurals — Page 21

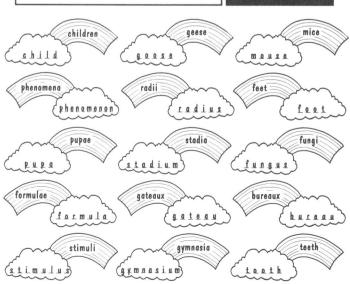

children — child
geese — goose
mice — mouse
phenomena — phenomenon
radii — radius
feet — foot
pupae — pupa
stadia — stadium
fungi — fungus
formulae — formula
gateaux — gateau
bureaux — bureau
stimuli — stimulus
gymnasia — gymnasium
teeth — tooth

Mysterious -ious!

dub|spac|prec|delic|malic|suspic ⑥

atroc|consc|ted|myster|delir|victor ⑥

fictit|infect|dev|obliv|ambit|nutrit|labor ⑦

1. __dub__ ious
2. __spac__ ious
3. __prec__ ious
4. __delic__ ious
5. __malic__ ious
6. __suspic__ ious
7. __atroc__ ious
8. __consc__ ious
9. __ted__ ious
10. __myster__ ious
11. __deli__ ious
12. __victor__ ious
13. __fictit__ ious
14. __infect__ ious
15. __dev__ ious
16. __obliv__ ious
17. __ambit__ ious
18. __nutrit__ ious
19. __labor__ ious

Root connections

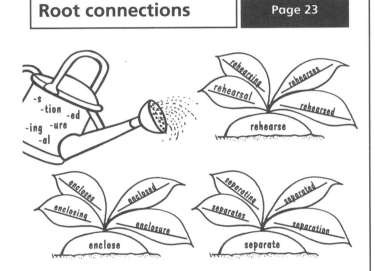

Language links

a	b	c	d	e	f	g	h	i	j	k	l	m	n	o	p	q	r	s	t	u	v	w	x	y	z
8	9	10	11	12	13	14	15	16	17	18	19	20	21	22	23	24	25	26	1	2	3	4	5	6	7

19-16-1-12-25-8-19 → l i t e r a l

23-8-25-8-14-25-8-23-15 → p a r a g r a p h

20-12-1-8-23-15-22-25 → m e t a p h o r

10-22-20-23-8-25-16-26-22-21 → c o m p a r i s o n

17-2-26-1-16-13-16-10-8-1-16-22-21 → j u s t i f i c a t i o n

16-21-13-12-25-12-21-10-12 → i n f e r e n c e

10-15-8-25-8-10-1-12-25-16-26-8-1-16-22-21 → c h a r a c t e r i s a t i o n

10-22-20-23-25-12-15-12-21-26-16-22-21 → c o m p r e h e n s i o n

10-22-21-1-12-5-1-2-8-19 → c o n t e x t u a l

20-22-1-16-3-8-1-16-22-21 → m o t i v a t i o n

22-23-16-21-16-22-21 → o p i n i o n

26-16-20-16-19-12 → s i m i l e

Maths measures

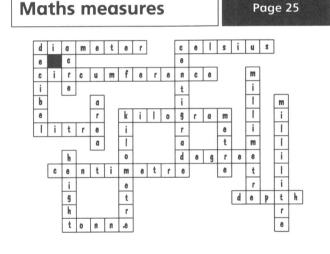

Worldly wise

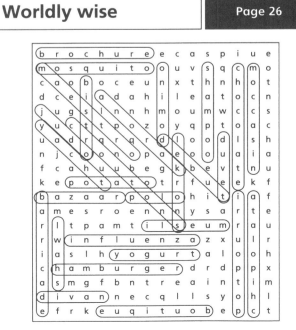

sidewalk / pavement / cab / taxi / movie / drugstore / chemist / film / Gasoline / petrol / firecracker / firework / fries / chips / candy / sweets / railroad / railway

■ Can you 'correct' these American spellings?

color	→	colour	gray	→	grey
center	→	centre	connexion	→	connection
humor	→	humour	flavor	→	flavour

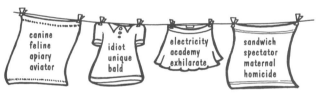

canine / feline / apiary / aviator — idiot / unique / bald — electricity / academy / exhilarate — sandwich / spectator / maternal / homicide

electricity — from Greek name for amber (elektron) which can be given a charge

sandwich — named after an earl so fond of gambling that he asked for lunch between two slices of bread to avoid stopping play

bold — originally meant you had a white patch – now used to indicate lack of hair

homicide — from Latin homicidium meaning 'manslaughter' and homo (man) + caedere (to kill)

idiot — from Greek idiotes meaning 'a common person'

apiary — a place to keep bees, from Latin apis meaning 'bee'

maternal — from Latin mater meaning 'mother'

academy — originally derived from the name of a legendary Greek hero call Academus

aviator — someone who flies, from Latin avis meaning 'bird'

feline — from Latin felis meaning 'cat'

canine — from Latin canis meaning 'dog'

exhilarate — from same Latin root as 'hilarious'

spectator — from Latin spectare meaning 'to look'

unique — from Latin unicus meaning 'one and only'

1. academy   2. apiary   3. aviator   4. bold   5. canine
6. electricity   7. exhilarate   8. feline   9. homicide   10. idiot
11. maternal   12. sandwich   13. spectator   14. unique

biscuit
foreign
restaurant
denim
alcohol
admiral
apostrophe
boycott
domino
glamour
handsome
migraine
rhinoceros
silhouette
earwig

■ Find the word from the list to match its meaning below.

1. __denim__ → name taken from the place it was first made (Serge de Nimes) in 17th century France
2. __biscuit__ → from medieval Latin bis coctus meaning 'twice baked'
3. __alcohol__ → from Arabic word meaning 'black powder' but now used to describe distilled spirits.
4. __foreign__ → from Latin word foranus meaning 'foreigner'
5. __restaurant__ → originally meant 'a food which restored'
6. __earwig__ → once believed wrongly that these insects could pierce the ear
7. __boycott__ → named after a person who was thrown out of a landowners club for charging too much rent
8. __domino__ → game named after Italian cry meaning 'winner!'
9. __apostrophe__ → from Greek meaning 'turned away', later used in punctuation for something missed out
10. __handsome__ → originally meaning 'pleasant to handle', now 'a pleasant appearance'
11. __migraine__ → from Greek for 'half skull', disease affecting one side of the head
12. __silhouette__ → named after a mean French politician who, to save money, only had outlines hanging in his house
13. __rhinoceros__ → from Greek meaning 'nose horn'
14. __glamour__ → by 19th century meant 'magic beauty'
15. __admiral__ → from Arabic amir meaning 'prince' or 'leader', changed due to similarity of word 'admire'

```
l e r e t h g u a l h c v n h k t p
m n p a r a g r a p h c o u u i e a
o e s q e t i x y a c r o n m l l i
e c y a a u w t o b a r i t a l e n
r i h c o u s a d m i t a i e l s a
o n h y b d r c i o a v n t e o c r
s p o k e a d e b a t e a i e r o s
c r l d r r a h m s s y v r e e p a
i s o t y v i t l s s y i c t r e t
e n g n u b r o c h u r e o o a t e
n o y o t a y g e i b u d m k f h s
t s m a t e r n a l s o e h m e g c
i b r e l e c t r h i o n g y r e o
f i c i n h e r i t i c r e v d a n
i s e d e c n a s i u n m e p i a f
c r r x m o g c i t i u a r t d t l
e u e c f u n g i e u l c x r a h i
l i h f i e x a g g e r a t e g i c
e t w r t q a c h i e v e e i i g t
c p e v i o l e n c e y w v i t n h
t q m z n w r i t e o r a v t n o x
i u o i g t a s n m e l o s c e n e
c y s e p a r a t e s e i f z c p t
```

New Spellaway 4

Key Stage 2

Answers

Influence of **ence**

■ Use the clues to complete these words which all end in **ence**.

#	Clue														
1.	Choosing one over another					f	e		e	n	c	e			
2.	A meeting for discussion			c		n			e	n	c	e			
3.	Distance round the outside of a circle		i	r			m	f			n		e		
4.	Dissimilarity					f	f		e	n					
5.	Formally begin						m	m		n					
6.	Done at your _____, or a W.C.					v	e	n			c				
7.	Requires a full stop at the end					s						e			
8.	Type of book for information					f	e		e			e			
9.	Moral sense or scruples					s	c			n		e			
10.	Extreme physical force					i	o		e		c				
11.	Treat yourself					d			g		n				
12.	State of not relying on others			d		p	e	n			c				
13.	Cheek!			i	m				e	n					
14.	Inability to wait						t	i	e	n	c	e			
15.	Harmlessness, freedom from guilt				n	n			e		c				

■ Use look, (say,) cover, write, check to practise each word.

_____   _____   _____

_____   _____   _____

_____   _____   _____

_____   _____   _____

_____

Tick here when you have checked your work. ☐

The **ance** alliance

■ Each **ance** word has been broken into its syllables.
Join them up again and practise each word.

word	syllable 1	syllable 2	syllable 3	
insurance	in	sur	ance	_____
grievance	griev	cum	stance	_____
circumstance	cir		ance	_____
substance	sub	a	stance	_____
guidance	guid	ppear	ance	_____
disappearance	dis	tten	ance	_____
extravagance	ex	a	dance	_____
entrance	en	trav	gance	_____
attendance	a		ance	_____
vengeance	ven	liv	trance	_____
exuberance	ex	fi	ance	_____
deliverance	de	ber	geance	_____
defiance	de	u	sance	_____
endurance	en	er	ance	_____
nuisance	nui	quain	ance	_____
acquaintance	ac	dur	tance	_____

Tick here when you have checked your work. ☐

Elementary discovery

■ **ery** and **ary** endings are often confused. Find these words in the puzzle to help you learn them.

```
b i d d a r y e r y k i n d
a n n i v e r s a r y c t c
c t c c r y l u b r r o r o
y r a t o r r c a q e n e r
r s p i a s t r p y n s a o
a u i o v e b e v r i t c n
r r l n o i c c u a h a h a
o g l a l z o o m r c b e r
p e a r u g o v w e a u r y
m r r y n h k e i t m l y r
e y y i t y e r x i o a e e
t w i a a y r l l n r o v
y a k r r f y i d y a y r o
r t y t y r t y r e l t u c
a e e e e a a y r e n e c s
x r e r r y r a n i l u c i
a y r y r a t n e m u c o d
```

anniversary _____

dictionary _____

capillary _____

coronary _____

library _____

rotary _____

constabulary _____

cutlery _____

culinary _____

voluntary _____

military _____

documentary _____

literary _____

temporary _____

cookery _____

discovery _____

watery _____

machinery _____

treachery _____

artery _____

recovery _____

surgery _____

scenery _____

■ Don't forget to use  **look, say, cover, write, check** to practise each word.

Tick here when you have checked your work. ☐

Vigorous OUS

■ Try to fit all these marvellous **ous** words into this puzzle.

unscrupulous ✓	carnivorous	unanimous	porous	courageous
bulbous	jealous	fabulous	humorous	
coniferous	ridiculous	famous	vigorous	

1. Absolutely great!	**u**
2. Agreeing without exception	**n**
3. Cone-bearing trees	**s**
4. Absurd	**c**
5. Funny	**r**
6. Swollen, bulging	**u**
7. Letting water through	**p**
8. Very brave	**u**
9. Green with envy	**l**
10. Meat eating	**o**
11. Well known	**u**
12. With energy	**s**

■ Use look, (say,) cover, write, check to practise all the words.

_____ _____ _____ _____

_____ _____ _____ _____

_____ _____ _____

Tick here when you have checked your work. ☐

■ Look in a dictionary to find the meaning of **unscrupulous**.

Puzzling plurals

■ The rainbows show the plural. You fill in the singular on the cloud. **Use a dictionary to check your spelling**.

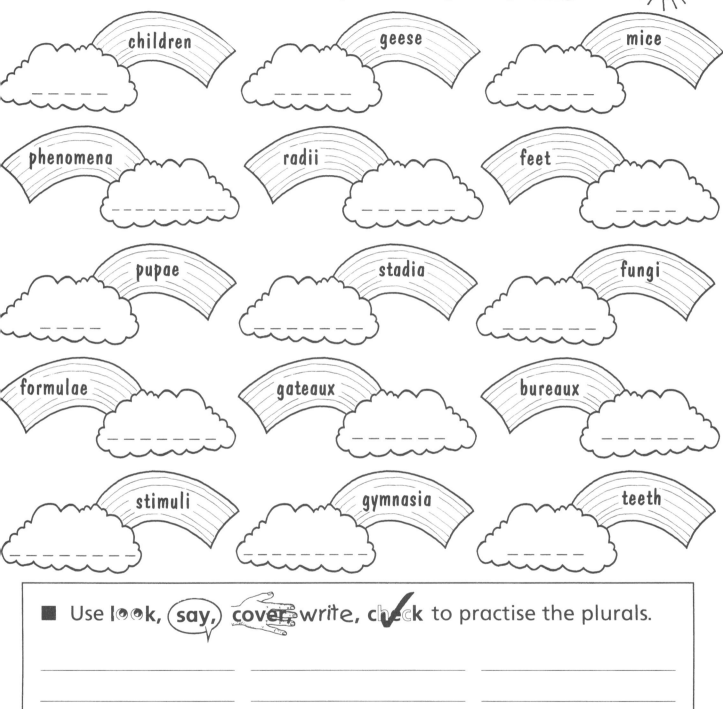

children __ __ __ __ __ __

geese __ __ __ __

mice __ __ __ __

phenomena __ __ __ __ __ __ __ __ __

radii __ __ __ __ __ __

feet __ __ __ __

pupae __ __ __ __

stadia __ __ __ __ __ __ __

fungi __ __ __ __ __

formulae __ __ __ __ __ __ __

gateaux __ __ __ __ __ __

bureaux __ __ __ __ __ __

stimuli __ __ __ __ __ __ __

gymnasium __ __ __ __ __ __ __ __

teeth __ __ __ __

■ Use look, (say,) cover, write, check to practise the plurals.

_____ _____ _____

_____ _____ _____

_____ _____ _____

_____ _____ _____

_____ _____ _____

Tick here when you have checked your work. ☐

Mysterious **ious**

ious

■ This curious creature has digested all the **ious** endings of these words. Find the beginnings to complete the list below.

dub/spacprecdelicmalicsuspic ⑥

atrocconsctedmysterdelirvictor ⑥

fictitinfectdevoblivambitnutritlabor ⑦

1. __dub__ ious
2. _____ ious
3. _____ ious
4. _____ ious
5. _____ ious

6. _____ ious
7. _____ ious
8. __consc__ ious
9. _____ ious
10. _____ ious

11. _____ ious
12. _____ ious
13. _____ ious
14. _____ ious
15. _____ ious

16. __obliv__ ious
17. _____ ious
18. _____ ious
19. _____ ious

■ Use look, (say,) cover, write, check to practise each word.

_____ _____ _____ _____

_____ _____ _____ _____

_____ _____ _____ _____

_____ _____ _____ _____

_____ _____ _____ _____

Tick here when you have checked your work. ☐

Root connections

We can add endings to verbs to show us when something is happening. Endings like **al**, **ure** and **tion** can change verbs into nouns.

■ Select endings from the watering can to grow three verbs and one noun from each root word.

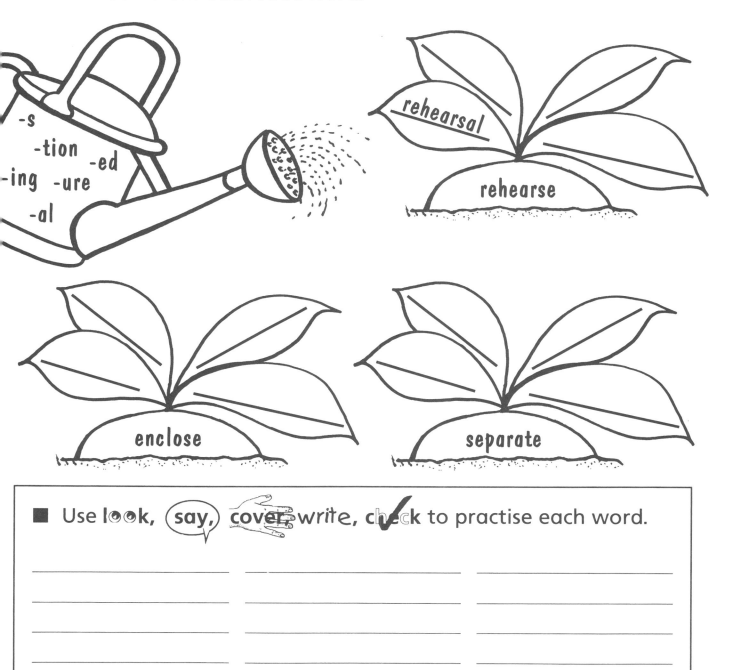

■ Use look, (say,) cover, write, check to practise each word.

_____ _____ _____

_____ _____ _____

_____ _____ _____

_____ _____ _____

_____ _____

Tick here when you have checked your work. ☐

Language links

- These words about language have been written in code.
  The code has been partly solved.
  Complete the code and use it to decode the words below.

a	b	c	d	e	f	g	h	i	j	k	l	m	n	o	p	q	r	s	t	u	v	w	x	y	z
	10	11	12	13	14	15		18	19									26						6	7

19·16·1·12·25·8·19

_ _ _ _ _ _ _

23·8·25·8·14·25·8·23·15

_ _ _ _ _ _ _ _ _

20·12·1·8·23·15·22·25

_ _ _ _ _ _ _ _

10·22·20·23·8·25·16·26·22·21

_ _ _ _ _ _ _ _ _ _

17·2·26·1·16·13·16·10·8·1·16·22·21

_ _ _ _ _ _ _ _ _ _ _ _ _

16·21·13·12·25·12·21·10·12

_ _ _ _ _ _ _ _ _

10·15·8·25·8·10·1·12·25·16·26·8·1·16·22·21

_ _ _ _ _ _ _ _ _ _ _ _ _ _ _ _

10·22·20·23·25·12·15·12·21·26·16·22·21

_ _ _ _ _ _ _ _ _ _ _ _ _

10·22·21·1·12·5·1·2·8·19

_ _ _ _ _ _ _ _ _ _

20·22·1·16·3·8·1·16·22·21

_ _ _ _ _ _ _ _ _ _

22·23·16·21·16·22·21

_ _ _ _ _ _ _

26·16·20·16·19·12

_ _ _ _ _ _

- Use look, (say,) cover, write, check to practise each word.

_____   _____   _____   _____

_____   _____   _____   _____

_____   _____   _____   _____

Tick here when you have checked your work. ☐

Maths measures

In mathematics there can be some tricky words to spell.

■ Practise these words by fitting them into the puzzle.

acre	circumference	height	millilitre
area	decibel	kilogram	millimetre
celsius	degree	kilometre	tonne
centigrade	depth	litre	
centimetre	diameter	metre	

■ Use look, (say,) cover, write, check to practise each word.

_____ _____ _____ _____

_____ _____ _____ _____

_____ _____ _____ _____

_____ _____ _____ _____

_____ _____

Tick here when you have checked your work. ☐

Worldly wise

■ Many of the words we use have been borrowed from other languages. If you search the puzzle you will discover 28 surprisingly familiar words.

anorak	influenza
barricade	judo
bazaar	maestro
bistro	moccasin
boutique	mosquito
brochure	muesli
chipolata	polo
chocolate	pot-pourri
croutons	potato
debut	shampoo
divan	shawl
domino	snorkel
duvet	yacht
hamburger	yogurt

```
b r o c h u r e e c a s p i u e
m o s q u i t o o u v s q c m o
c a o b o c e u n x t h n h o t
d c e i a d a h i l e a t o c n
j u g s l n n h m o u m w c c s
y u c t t p o z o y q p t o a c
u a d r q r q r d l o o d l s h
n j c o o n o p a e o o u a i a
f c a h u u b e g k b e v t n u
k e p o t a t o t r f u e e k f
b a z a a r p o l o h i t i a f
a m e s r o e n n n y s a r t e
r l t p a m t i l s e u m r a u
r w i n f l u e n z a z x u l r
i a s l h y o g u r t a l o o h
c h a m b u r g e r d r d p p x
a s m g f b n t r e a i n t i m
d i v a n n e c q l l s y o h l
e f r k e u q i t u o b e p c t
```

■ Now try to find where each word came from. Use a good dictionary or encyclopedia.

■ Use look, (say,) cover, write, check to practise each word.

_____ _____ _____ _____ _____

_____ _____ _____ _____ _____

_____ _____ _____ _____ _____

_____ _____ _____ _____ _____

_____ _____ _____

Tick here when you have checked your work. ☐

American angle ⭐🇺🇸

Although Americans speak English, they often spell words differently and use different vocabulary.

■ Complete the English translations of the American words below using the vowels to help you.

sidewalk
_ a _ e _ e _ _ _

cab
_ a _

movie
_ _ i _

Coke
_ _ _ e _ i _ _ _ _ (drugstore)

drugstore
_ _ _ e _ i _ _

firecracker
_ i _ e _ o _ _ _

fries
_ _ i _ _

candy
_ _ _ e e _ _

Gasoline
_ e _ _ o _

railroad
_ a i _ _ _ _ _

■ Can you 'correct' these American spellings?

color → _____   gray → _____

center → _____   connexion → _____

humor → _____   flavor → _____

■ Use **look**, (**say,**) **cover**, **write**, **check** to practise the English words.

_____ _____ _____

_____ _____ _____

_____ _____ _____

_____ _____ _____

Tick here when you have checked your work. ☐

Historic hints – hang on!

vocabulary extension + comprehension

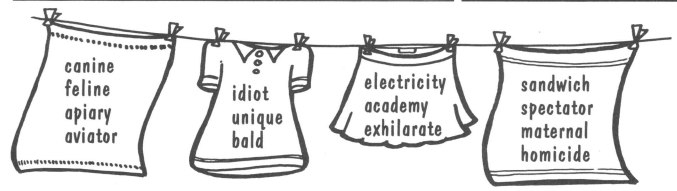

canine
feline
apiary
aviator

idiot
unique
bald

electricity
academy
exhilarate

sandwich
spectator
maternal
homicide

■ Search the washing line for the word to fit each definition in a basket.

- from Greek name for amber (*elektron*) which can be given a charge
- named after an earl so fond of gambling that he asked for lunch between two slices of bread to avoid stopping play
- originally meant you had a white patch – now used to indicate lack of hair
- from Latin *homicidium* meaning 'manslaughter' and *homo* (man) + *caedere* (to kill)

- from Greek *idiotes* meaning 'a common person'
- a place to keep bees, from Latin *apis* meaning 'bee'
- from Latin *mater* meaning 'mother'
- originally derived from the name of a legendary Greek hero call Academus
- someone who flies, from Latin *avis* meaning 'bird'

- from Latin *felix* meaning 'cat'
- from Latin *canis* meaning 'dog'
- from same Latin root as 'hilarious'
- from Latin *spectare* meaning 'to look'
- from Latin *unicus* meaning 'one and only'

■ Arrange all the words from the washing line in alphabetical order.

1._____ 2._____ 3._____ 4._____ 5._____

6._____ 7._____ 8._____ 9._____ 10._____

11._____ 12._____ 13._____ 14._____

■ Use look, (say,) cover, write, check to practise these words.

_____ _____ _____ _____

_____ _____ _____ _____

_____ _____ _____ _____

Tick here when you have checked your work. ☐

Page 28

Odd origins

odd origins of words

| biscuit |
| foreign |
| restaurant |
| denim |
| alcohol |
| admiral |
| apostrophe |
| boycott |
| domino |
| glamour |
| handsome |
| migraine |
| rhinoceros |
| silhouette |
| earwig |

■ Find the word from the list to match its meaning below.

1. _____ → name taken from the place it was first made (Serge de Nimes) in 17th century France

2. _____ → from medieval Latin *bis coctus* meaning 'twice baked'

3. _____ → from Arabic word meaning 'black powder' but now used to describe distilled spirits.

4. _____ → from Latin word *foranus* meaning 'foreigner'

5. _____ → originally meant 'a food which restored'

6. _____ → once believed wrongly that these insects could pierce the ear

7. _____ → named after a person who was thrown out of a landowners club for charging too much rent

8. _____ → game named after Italian cry meaning 'winner!'

9. _____ → from Greek meaning 'turned away', later used in punctuation for something missed out

10. _____ → originally meaning 'pleasant to handle', now 'a pleasant appearance'

11. _____ → from Greek for 'half skull', disease affecting one side of the head

12. _____ → named after a mean French politician who, to save money, only had outlines hanging in his house

13. _____ → from Greek meaning 'nose horn'

14. _____ → by 19th century meant 'magic beauty'

15. _____ → from Arabic *amir* meaning 'prince' or 'leader', changed due to similarity of word 'admire'

■ Use look, (say,) cover, write, check to practise all the words.

_____ _____ _____ _____ _____

_____ _____ _____ _____ _____

_____ _____ _____ _____ _____

Tick here when you have checked your work. ☐

Mega mind blower

■ All these words have been used in *New Spellaway*.
Find them in the wordsearch on the facing page.
They may be hidden in all directions.

about	extravagance	restaurant
accident	fierce	said
achieve	foreign	scene
biscuit	formulae	scientific
brochure	fungi	separates
ceiling	humour	shirt
centigrade	hyperactive	solemn
chaos	inherit	somewhere
colour	kilometre	sore
conflict	laughter	spoke
courage	maternal	stomach
dairy	motivation	substitute
debate	nought	telescope
debut	nuisance	treachery
electric	other	violence
exaggerate	paragraph	voluntary
exciting	piece	write
exhilarate	psychology	

Mega mind blower

```
l e r e t h g u a l h c v n h k t p
m n p a r a g r a p h o o n u i e a
o e s q e t i x y a c u l o m l l i
e c y a a u w t o b a r u i o o e t
r e c e c o u s a d m a n t u m s n
o i h i h b d r c i o g t a r e c a
s p o k e a d e b a t e a v k t o r
c r l d r r a h m s s o r i e r p u
i s o t y v i t l s s y y t c e e a
e p g n u b r o c h u r e o n k c t
n o y o t a y g e i b u d m a m o s
t m a t e r n a l r s o e h g r n e
i s a c c i d e n t t l f y a c f r
f b r e l e c t r h i o o p v j l e
i i c i n h e r i t t c r e a e i t
c s e d e c n a s i u n m r r d c a
e c r r x m o g c i t i u a t a t r
l u e e c f u n g i e u l c x r t a
e i h f i e x a g g e r a t e g h l
c t w r t q a c h i e v e i e i g i
t p e v i o l e n c e y w v i t u h
r q m z n w r i t e o r a e c n o x
i u o i g t a s n m e l o s c e n e
c y s e p a r a t e s e i f z c p t
```

Congratulations!
You have now finished the New Spellaway series!

Schofield&Sims

the long-established educational publisher
specialising in maths, English and science materials for schools

New Spellaway is a series of graded activity books containing puzzles and activities designed to reinforce spelling using the widely recommended 'look, say, cover, write, check' method.

New Spellaway Book 4 includes:

- Prefixes (for example, 'sub' at the start of a word)
- Syllables
- Homophones (words spelt differently but sounding the same)
- Irregular past tenses
- Changing verbs into nouns (for example, adding 'al', 'ure' or 'tion' to the ends of words).

This book is suitable for children in Key Stage 2.

The full range of titles in the series is as follows:

New Spellaway Book 1:   ISBN 978 07217 0847 8

New Spellaway Book 2:   ISBN 978 07217 0848 5

New Spellaway Book 3:   ISBN 978 07217 0849 2

New Spellaway Book 4:   ISBN 978 07217 0850 8

Have you tried **Springboard** by Schofield & Sims?
This is a series of graded activity books reinforcing key aspects of literacy such as sentence construction, vocabulary and reading comprehension.

**For further information and to place your order
visit www.schofieldandsims.co.uk or telephone 01484 607080**

ISBN 978-07217-0850-8

9 780721 708508

Schofield&Sims

Dogley Mill, Fenay Bridge, Huddersfield HD8 0NQ
Phone: 01484 607080 Facsimile: 01484 606815
E-mail: sales@schofieldandsims.co.uk
www.schofieldandsims.co.uk

ISBN 978 07217 0850 8

**£2.45
(Retail price)**

Key Stage 2
Age range: 7–11 years